From Bump to Baby

LTP
London

From Bump to Baby

LTP
London

Keep treasured memories safe
as you embark on the most exciting
adventure of your life!

This gorgeous journal has space to record all the
special moments of your own unique pregnancy journey,
and helps you unwind as you write down your feelings,
hopes and dreams for the future arrival. The week-by-
week development updates will keep you informed
of your baby's progression, and the useful tips
and resources will aid you in the truly magical
transition from bump to baby.

My name is

....

And I'm going to be a **mummy!**

I'm Pregnant!

Date I found out I was pregnant:

How far gone I was:

How I knew:

I felt:

Who I told first and their reactions:

Early Days

Your pregnancy is counted from the first day of your last period, which means that in the first two weeks or so, you aren't actually pregnant! But once the embryo has implanted in the lining of the womb, development of your baby will start in earnest.

Week 5

This would be the first week of the missed period, and is when many women begin to suspect that they might be pregnant. Although only 2mm long at this stage, the embryo is beginning to develop its own nervous system and blood vessels.

Week 6

Now with a thin layer of see-through skin and a tiny beating heart, the embryo is growing rapidly.

Week 7

The embryo is 10mm and growing bigger every day, and the brain is developing at an incredible rate. It is also beginning to form cartilage, which will soon become the bones of the legs and arms.

Week 8

The embryo is now a foetus, which means 'offspring', and is looking more like a baby each day. The head is growing bigger and the legs are lengthening.

Week 9

Your baby is now around 22mm long, and has formed a face including a mouth and tongue with tiny taste buds.

Week 10

The ears are starting to develop and there is now a jawbone, which already contains all of the milk teeth!

Week 11

The bones of the face are fully formed, and your baby will now have fingers and toes, complete with little fingernails.

My Baby's First Picture!

At around 12 weeks you'll finally get to see your baby!
The sonographer may also be able to give you a due date
to let you know when to expect your little bundle of joy.
Put a copy of the scan picture here.

Date of the scan: ....

How I felt when I first saw Baby: ....

....

....

My baby's due date is: ....

Week 12

Baby is about the size of an apricot!

5.4 cm

14g

What has changed with Baby:

Your baby's reflexes are developing! She can now curl her fingers and toes and clench her eye muscles. Although you won't feel her moving yet, she'll wriggle if you give your belly a prod. She's also been practising her breathing, and her face is beginning to look more human.

What has changed with Mummy:

You're now moving out of your first trimester, which means a lot of uncomfortable symptoms such as nausea will soon stop - hooray! It won't be long until your beautiful baby bump starts blooming, so it may be time to look into looser clothing.

How I'm feeling: ....

....

What I've been doing: ....

....

....

Tips: Now is a good time to start doing pelvic floor exercises, which will help with labour and birth when the time comes.

Week 13

Baby is around the size of a plum!

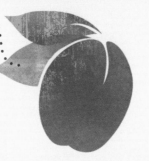

7.62cm   25.5g

What has changed with Baby:

Baby's still pretty tiny, so it's hard to believe that his genitalia are now fully developed, dictating whether you're having a girl or a boy – though this won't show up on a scan for a few weeks yet.

What has changed with Mummy:

At the end of this week you'll officially be in your second trimester, which should be more comfortable than the first. You're a third of the way through! Your pregnancy symptoms might disappear altogether, but your slowly growing tummy will leave little room for doubt.

How I'm feeling: ....

....

What I've been doing: ....

....

....

Tips: If you're feeling more like yourself, now could be a good time to start re-introducing a little light exercise to help keep in shape.

Sharing the News

Around now it's common to start letting people know your news, although timing is completely up to you. Whenever you do it, write down the details of your announcement here – and some of the best reactions!

Week 14

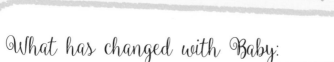

Baby is roughly the size of a lemon!

8.92cm   45.4g

What has changed with Baby:

Baby's had a growth spurt since last week and has almost doubled in weight! She's also beginning to grow hair, and her facial muscles are getting a work out as she practises squinting, frowning, and grimacing. She may even be able to suck her thumb!

What has changed with Mummy:

Your appetite might start to increase any time in your second trimester, so look after your growing bump and keep healthy with plenty of fruit, vegetables and nuts. Sadly eating for two is a myth!

How I'm feeling: ....

....

What I've been doing: ....

....

....

Tips: For a tasty, healthy snack, try putting frozen banana in the blender, and add a topping of your choice.

Cravings

Lots of women find that they develop cravings for certain foods, and aversions to others, at different points in their pregnancy. Use this space to record the foods that have been making you lick your lips or turning your stomach!

Week 15

Baby is around the size of a peach

 10.59cm

 72.6g

What has changed with Baby:

Baby's legs have started to grow faster than his arms, and he can now move all his joints and limbs. Even though his eyes are still closed, he's beginning to become sensitive to bright lights, and he may start to be able to hear the sound of your heartbeat.

What has changed with Mummy:

Typically energy levels are high at 15 weeks, so hopefully you'll be feeling great! But heartburn, nosebleeds and swollen gums are all normal at this stage, all of which you can blame on your hormones. It's not all bad though, as shiny, thick hair is one of the common pregnancy perks.

How I'm feeling: ....

....

What I've been doing: ....

....

....

Tips: If pregnancy hormones have left you a little gassy, try avoiding foods like broccoli, cabbage and beans.

Symptoms and Side Effects

By week 15 you're well into the swing of your pregnancy, and may have started to notice a wide array of unexpected side effects. Most of these will be common, for example a blocked nose due to the increased blood flow to your mucus membranes, but don't be afraid to ask your midwife if there's anything you're not sure about. Note down your pregnancy symptoms here.

Talking to Baby

By 16 weeks, Baby will start to be able to hear your voice. It's strange to think it, but soon she'll also start listening to other noises from the outside world. Use this space to record sounds you like to share with your baby.

Things I like to say to my bump:

Other sounds or music I share with my baby:

Week 16

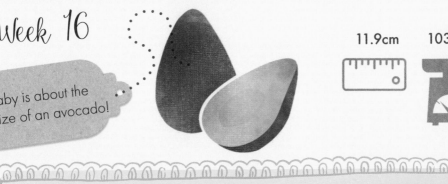

Baby is about the size of an avocado!

11.9cm   103.8g

What has changed with Baby:

Your baby's hands can now form a fist or hold each other when they touch, and she might even be practising her reflexes by grabbing hold of the umbilical cord!

What has changed with Mummy:

Around this time you might start sensing your baby move, though it may just feel like a flutter or bubbling to begin with. The coveted 'pregnancy glow' should also be within your reach as your hair and nails grow faster, and thanks to an increase in hormones and blood volume your skin is radiant!

How I'm feeling: ....

....

What I've been doing: ....

....

....

Tips: Many women experience heartburn at this stage. To help avoid this, try eating smaller meals more frequently, as well as avoiding spicy or greasy foods.

Week 17

Baby is about the size of an apple!

13.3cm   142.3g

What has changed with Baby:

Baby's continuing to develop sight, smell, touch and sound senses. His arms and legs have reached their normal proportions, and his skeleton has begun to harden into bone. He's preparing himself to grow up big and strong!

What has changed with Mummy:

As your uterus expands and puts pressure on the nearby ligaments, you may experience slight pain in your pelvis and lower stomach. It's not unusual for this rapid growth to also make you feel a bit off-balance!

How I'm feeling: ....

....

What I've been doing: ....

....

....

Tips: Now is a wise time to switch to flat or low-heeled shoes, and if you have ligament pain consider getting a maternity belt to support your bump and baby.

Dreams

Due to disrupted sleep around the 17 week mark it's common to start having very vivid dreams, which can often be a little strange! Record your dreams or night-time thoughts and feelings below.

What I have been dreaming about:

Week 18

Baby is roughly the size of an orange!

14.4cm 170.9g

What has changed with Baby:

Baby is very active now, twisting, rolling, punching and kicking, and you may well be able to feel it! She also yawns and hiccups, and can both suck and swallow.

What has changed with Mummy:

You may find you experience backache caused by the pressure and position of your growing baby. From this point on, it is recommended that you sleep on your left side, as this allows for maximum flow of blood and will ease the strain on your back.

How I'm feeling: ....

....

What I've been doing: ....

....

....

Tips: Try using pillows between your knees, under your bump and behind your back, to help you get comfy and prop you onto your left side at night.

Baby's First Kick

The first time you feel your baby move is a special moment you'll never want to forget! Those first fluttery movements can happen any time between 16 and 20 weeks. Note down when you first felt Baby move and your thoughts and feelings here:

Time to Unwind

With so much changing, it's normal to feel a bit anxious and stressed. Plenty of rest, gentle exercise or even a pregnancy massage can help you unwind. Note down the things that help you feel relaxed here.

Exercise that helps me relax:

Other things that help me unwind:

Week 19

Baby is around the size of an onion!

15.7cm **243.2g**

What has changed with Baby:

Your baby's eyes are still closed but he's beginning to grow eyelashes and eyebrows, and his fingers and toes are fully developed. Around this time, his very own unique fingerprints will be forming.

What has changed with Mummy:

It's common to feel tired as the stresses and strains of pregnancy disturb your sleep, so try to find time to relax in the day. By now your baby bump is blooming, and that's a great excuse to enjoy showing it off in your new maternity clothes!

How I'm feeling: ....

....

What I've been doing: ....

Tips: If leg cramps are troubling you, try extending your leg and flexing your ankle and toes towards your knee to ease the pain.

....

....

Week 20

Baby is about the size of a pomegranate!

 26cm 303.1g

What has changed with Baby:

Your baby's skin now has the greasy coating which will protect it in the womb. She will also have fine hair all over her body, but this usually disappears before birth.

What has changed with Mummy:

Congratulations, you have reached the halfway point of your pregnancy! You may find you need to rest more as the weeks go by, and limit the amount of time you are on your feet. If possible, take short, frequent breaks from activity and enjoy a well-deserved rest.

How I'm feeling: ....

....

What I've been doing: ....

....

....

Tips: Iron is important to make extra blood for your baby. Make sure you eat plenty of iron-rich foods such as lean red meat, poultry, fish, lentils, spinach, and iron-fortified cereals.

My Baby's Second Picture!

At around 20 weeks you'll get another glimpse of your bundle of joy. The sonographer will check how Baby is developing, and if you want to know, may even be able to tell you if you are having a boy or a girl! Put a copy of the scan picture here.

Date of the scan: ....

How I felt when I saw my baby: ....

....

....

My decision about knowing Baby's gender: ....

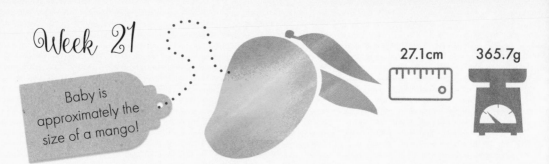

Week 21

Baby is approximately the size of a mango!

27.1cm   365.7g

What has changed with Baby:

Baby now has his own pattern of sleep, and he may be awake and active when you are trying to sleep! As his nervous system begins to work effectively, he is becoming more aware every day.

What has changed with Mummy:

Your uterus is now at the level of your belly button. You may develop a dark line called a linea nigra down the middle of your tummy and chest, which is just normal skin pigmentation as your bump expands.

How I'm feeling: ....

....

What I've been doing: ....

....

....

Tips: Attending antenatal classes is a great way to help prepare for birth and meet other mums-to-be.

Relax and Enjoy Your Bump!

This trimester can be the most enjoyable time in your pregnancy. You are not too big yet, and the uncomfortable symptoms like fatigue and nausea are mostly gone. Use this space to record the things you most enjoy about being pregnant.

Baby Names!

You have probably thought lots about names already, but now may be the time to start narrowing down your list. Note down your ideas here.

Names I have considered:

My favourite 5 names:

Week 22

Baby is around the size of a cucumber!

28cm

434.3g

What has changed with Baby:

Now that Baby's eyes and lips are more developed, she is looking even more like a newborn every day. Even at this early stage, the first sign of Baby's teeth are appearing in the form of tooth buds beneath the gum line.

What has changed with Mummy:

Due to hormonal changes, you may be experiencing 'pregnancy brain' and have trouble concentrating or feel forgetful. Try not to over-plan and only prioritise the most important things, as stress can make forgetfulness worse.

How I'm feeling: ....

....

What I've been doing: ....

....

....

Tips: Your change in hormones also makes you more prone to urinary infections. To keep them at bay, try drinking a daily glass of unsweetened cranberry juice.

Week 23

Baby is roughly the size of a grapefruit!

29.2cm   512.6g

What has changed with Baby:

Baby's skin pigment is changing to its final colour and you might be able to feel that his feet are kicking more often and with more force! Although he's still getting all his oxygen from you via the placenta, his lungs are practising breathing movements ready for life outside the womb.

What has changed with Mummy:

It's common for pregnancy hormones to make you more emotional than usual, and you may be feeling clumsy as your centre of gravity has shifted. If you need a pick-me-up, these middle months are the perfect time to fit in a holiday, so start planning your babymoon!

How I'm feeling: ....

....

What I've been doing: ....

....

....

Tips: Don't forget to keep up with your pelvic floor exercises, as they will help you to avoid stress incontinence after birth.

Emotions

Pregnancy has many emotional ups and downs. Taking time out, talking to other mums or writing down your feelings can help you feel better. Use this space for recording your thoughts and feelings on your pregnancy journey so far.

Week 24

Baby is almost the size of a coconut!

 30.5cm   630.5g

What has changed with Baby:

Your baby is now so well-developed that she could potentially survive outside the womb with neonatal care. Her brain is growing rapidly and her lungs are developing. The next few weeks will be key for Baby to put on weight and for all her vital organs to mature.

What has changed with Mummy:

You may have begun to experience rib pain as your growing uterus pushes your organs up into your rib cage. Another common side-effect is the appearance of red stretch marks, but these should fade after birth, and like all the other niggles of pregnancy will be forgotten once you have your baby to hold!

How I'm feeling: ....

....

What I've been doing: ....

....

Tips: Try an anti-stretch mark cream or oil to minimize the appearance of stretch marks. Eating healthily and taking gentle exercise to avoid unnecessary weight gain will help too.

Nesting!

From around this time, you might be focused on organising your home for a new little person! Note some of your plans and preparations.

My ideas for Baby's nursery:

Other home changes I am thinking about:

My Pregnancy Pictures

Your pregnancy lasts for such a short amount of time that you'll want to keep as many physical memories as possible. You are really blooming now, and before long, your bump will be gone and you'll be holding your baby! Stick some of your pregnancy photos here.

Week 25

Baby is about the size of a papaya!

32.8cm **675.9g**

What has changed with Baby:

Baby is growing plumper each day and his skin is looking smoother and less wrinkly. His senses are becoming more sophisticated too, and if you shine a gentle light on your tummy, your baby will turn his head towards it.

What has changed with Mummy:

As Baby takes up more space, you may get indigestion and find it difficult to eat large meals. Your body is working hard right now, so it's a great time to enjoy some pampering, and book that pedicure or pregnancy massage!

How I'm feeling: ....

....

What I've been doing: ....

Tips: Trips to the bathroom may be keeping you up at night, so try drinking extra water earlier in the day and then tapering off your intake closer to bedtime.

....

Week 26

Baby is around the size of a head of broccoli!

35.5cm **725.7g**

What has changed with Baby:

If they haven't already, soon your baby's eyes will open. Even though it may not feel like it, she still has plenty of room to move around and may even be doing full somersaults!

What has changed with Mummy:

You may start to experience Braxton Hicks contractions around this time, which is when your bump occasionally feels really tight. These are practise contractions that tone your uterus ready for labour. They are different from labour contractions, though, as they will be irregular and mild.

How I'm feeling: ....

....

What I've been doing: ....

....

....

Tips: Baby's brain is developing fast at this stage, so your nutrition will be more important than ever. Continue to eat a well-balanced diet that includes plenty of grains and vegetables.

Antenatal Classes

You might soon be starting antenatal classes. As well as learning lots about birth and caring for your newborn, you'll hopefully make some new mum friends too! Keep a note of some of the things you have learnt and enjoyed here.

People I have met in the class:

The most important things I learnt:

Things I would like to find out more about:

Holidays

You may be going on a babymoon to enjoy some couple time before your little one arrives, or perhaps you are fitting in a spa break for some well-deserved me-time. Use this space to save pictures from any pre-baby trips you take.

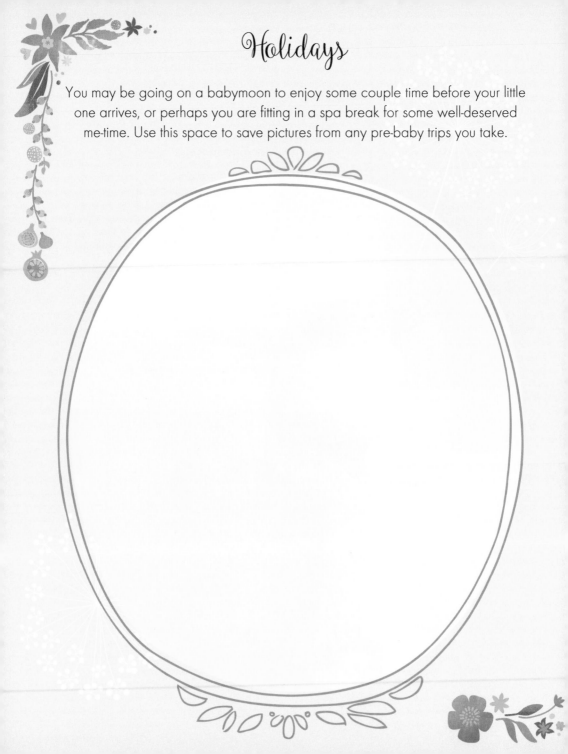

Week 27

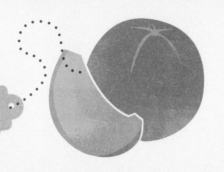

Baby is roughly the size of a cantaloupe!

37.3cm   884.5g

What has changed with Baby:

No one knows for sure, but it's possible that your baby will start having dreams around this time. Baby's brain is certainly active now, and will be able to undertake more and more complex functions as the tissue develops.

What has changed with Mummy:

The size of your growing baby may be making you feel short of breath, and as he is pressing hard on your bladder, you'll need lots of pit stops. But hang on in there, as you are about to enter your third trimester, and it won't be long before you meet your baby!

How I'm feeling: ....

....

What I've been doing: ....

....

....

Tips: Baby will probably be giving you a few sharp prods by now, but this is a great sign that he is thriving. Enjoy relaxing in bed or in the bath and watch your bump – you'll be surprised at how much it moves about!

Use this space to note down your thoughts and feelings on your second trimester.

....
....
....
....
....
....
....
....
....
....
....
....
....
....
....
....
....
....
....

Antenatal Appointments

In this final stage of pregnancy, you'll have more antenatal check-ups than before. These are often at 28, 31, 34, 36, 38, and 40 weeks (and 41 weeks if you go overdue). Use this space to note down your appointment times, and any questions you may have for your midwife.

Week 28

Baby is approximately the size of an aubergine!

38.1cm   1038.7g

What has changed with Baby:

Baby is continuing to gain fat and her bones are nearly developed, though they won't harden properly for a few weeks yet. The sleep-wake pattern she now has will be very similar once she is born, so take note!

What has changed with Mummy:

Welcome to your third trimester! Your feelings are probably switching between excitement at meeting your baby and anxiety about labour and coping with a newborn. Taking time to relax each day is really important to promote feelings of calm, and ticking things off your to-do list can help you feel in control.

How I'm feeling: ....

....

What I've been doing: ....

....

....

Tips: Having trouble sleeping is normal during the third trimester. Try to do something relaxing like reading a book or having a cup of chamomile tea to help you nod off again.

Week 29

Baby is the size of a butternut squash!

39.4cm

1165.7g

What has changed with Baby:

Your baby's head is getting bigger to make room for his developing brain. Though he now weighs more than a kilo, he will triple in weight over the coming weeks before birth!

What has changed with Mummy:

Now is a great time to enjoy planning your maternity leave, and look into breastfeeding or mum and baby classes. This could help take your mind off any unpleasant symptoms you may be experiencing, such as heartburn and hemorrhoids, due to Baby putting pressure on your digestive system.

How I'm feeling: ....

....

What I've been doing: ....

....

....

Tips: If you are experiencing mild headaches, difficulty sleeping could be the cause but it could also be low blood sugar. Eating at regular intervals could help you manage this.

Baby's Birthplace

If you're thinking of giving birth in a hospital or midwife unit, it's a great idea to take a look around as well as talking to other mums who have given birth there. Use this space to note down any questions or thoughts you may have on possible locations.

Week 30

Baby is around the size of a cauliflower!

40.4cm   1333.6g

What has changed with Baby:

By now, your baby's brain is developing separate areas that will control specific functions. She is surrounded by about a litre of amniotic fluid, and the amniotic sac has now reached its full size. As Baby fills out your uterus, the fluid will soon start to decrease.

What has changed with Mummy:

Thanks to more fluid circulating and making your body tissues thicken, you may feel a bit swollen or puffy in your ankles, legs, fingers, neck or face. But as long as it's not sudden or severe, this is totally normal.

How I'm feeling: ....

....

What I've been doing: ....

....

....

Tips: You should notice that people are starting to offer you seats wherever you go. Be sure to take them up on this – as well as being a perk of pregnancy, you need all the rest you can get.

Bouncing Baby

All babies have their own pattern of movement in the womb, so why not note down the times of day (or night!) your baby feels most active.
If you notice that your baby isn't moving as usual, always contact your midwife for reassurance and a check-up.

My baby's sleep/wake patterns:

Week 31

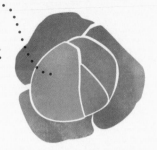

Baby is about the size of a cabbage!

41.5cm 1519.5g

What has changed with Baby:

Baby's sucking reflex has now fully developed, so he is probably enjoying sucking his thumb or fingers! His nervous system has also matured, so he can control his own body temperature rather than relying on the temperature of the amniotic fluid.

What has changed with Mummy:

Your breasts are going through some remarkable changes to prepare to be able to feed your baby. They may feel larger, fuller and more sensitive, and the area around the nipples will darken so Baby can see them better when the time comes to feed.

How I'm feeling: ....

....

What I've been doing: ....

....

....

Tips: A well-fitting pregnancy bra is essential to keep you comfy. Try putting tissue or absorbent nursing pads in your bra to catch any leaks.

Planning for Baby's Birth

As you are now in your third trimester the final weeks of your pregnancy will fly by, so take some time to think about your baby's birth. Note down your thoughts and feelings below.

Where I would like to give birth and why:

Who I would like to be with me:

Thoughts on different pain relief options:

Positions that may help me in labour and birth:

Last Minute Shopping

Around this time you'll want to make sure you've got everything you need for labour and immediately after. The list of ideas on Week 34 may help you to remember anything you've forgotten.

Things to buy for myself and for my birth partner:

Things left to buy for Baby:

Week 32

Baby is roughly the size of a pineapple!

43.3cm   1728.2g

What has changed with Baby:

By this week, Baby's toenails and fingernails will have developed to their final form. She may now be lying in the head-down position ready for birth. If she's not yet head-down, don't worry, as there is still time for her to turn.

What has changed with Mummy:

Changes in blood circulation may cause heart palpitations, which are runs of fast heartbeats or missing a beat occasionally. These are usually nothing to worry about but if you also experience shortness of breath or chest pain, you should contact your doctor.

Tips: Make sure you have a car seat ready for Baby's first trip home. It may be a good idea to install it now just in case you have an early arrival!

How I'm feeling: ....

....

What I've been doing: ....

....

....

Week 33

Baby is roughly the size of a honeydew melon!

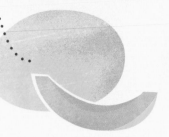

44.8cm   1950.4g

What has changed with Baby:

The bones in your baby's body are now hardening, except for the bones in his skull which remain soft and pliable until after birth. During birth they will gently move and overlap to allow Baby to descend the birth canal.

What has changed with Mummy:

You are probably feeling hot about now, and this is a normal reaction to your increased metabolic rate. After birth this will return to normal, but until then wear light layers, drink plenty of water, and perhaps invest in a hand-held fan to help you keep cool.

How I'm feeling: ....

....

What I've been doing: ....

....

Tips: Constipation is a common symptom around this time. Eating plenty of fresh fruit and vegetables, keeping hydrated and gentle exercise should help keep you regular!

Baby Essentials

Check you are ready for Baby's arrival and have stocked up on all the essentials for a newborn! Take a look at the list towards the back of the book and jot down any final things you need to get.

Week 34

Baby is about the size of a bunch of celery!

46cm   2186.3g

What has changed with Baby:

Baby's digestive enzymes are now active and ready to process milk, and her arms and legs are fattening up. Your baby may 'engage' from this week, which is when she descends lower into the pelvis in the position for birth, though some babies do not do this until labour begins.

What has changed with Mummy:

If your baby has engaged you may feel you can breathe easily again. This is called 'lightening' – the sudden sensation of having more space to breathe now Baby has moved down. The flipside is that Baby will be pressing harder on your bladder, meaning even more trips to the bathroom!

How I'm feeling: ....

....

What I've been doing: ....

....

....

Tips: Now is your chance to make the most of time to yourself and with your partner. So book that haircut or manicure, and indulge in meals out and trips to the cinema.

Hospital Bag Checklist

Having your hospital bag packed in advance will help you feel well prepared for the birth of your baby. It's a good idea to have everything ready a few weeks before your due date, just in case Baby makes an early appearance. The essentials are listed below.

For you:

- Birth plan or medical notes.

- A loose and comfortable outfit for you to wear during labour – cotton is a good choice if you're worried about being too hot.

- Dressing gown and slippers.

- Front-opening tops or nightwear if you're planning to breastfeed.

- Five or six pairs of pants (disposable or old ones are best) and socks.

- A few comfy and supportive bras (nursing bras if you're planning to breastfeed). Remember to factor in that your breasts will have grown between packing the bag and labour!

- Maternity and nursing pads.

- Toiletries including a gentle soap or shower gel, toothbrush, hairbrush, and hairbands or clips for keeping your hair off your face.

- Towels and pillows if you need them.

- Books, magazines or a playlist to help you pass the time and relax.

- A handheld fan, sponge or water spray that your birthing partner can use to cool you down.

- A loose coming-home outfit to wear after you have given birth.

- Snacks and drinks for you and your birthing partner – giving birth is hungry work!

For Baby:

- Clothes and nappies. Don't forget a hat!

- A shawl or blanket to wrap your baby in.

- Cotton wool or baby wipes.

Caring for Your Newborn

A newborn baby requires constant care, and you're bound to have a bit of an adjustment period while you get to grips with your baby's needs. There are lots of little tips and tricks you can learn from your midwife, so use this space to write down any questions you may have, or things you're unsure of.

Aspects of caring for my baby I would like to know more about:

Questions I have for my midwife:

Week 35

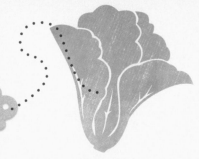

Baby is roughly the size of a romaine lettuce!

47.3cm 2417.6g

What has changed with Baby:

From this point on, Baby will not increase much in length but he will continue plumping up and gaining weight. Your baby's pupils can now dilate if the sun or bright light filter into the uterus.

What has changed with Mummy:

You may find yourself leaning back to compensate for the heavy weight of your baby, and walking may become more of a waddle as you shift weight from side to side. Your uterus has now increased to an incredible 1,000 times its original size, though by the sixth week after birth it will be right back to normal again!

How I'm feeling: ....

....

What I've been doing: ....

....

Tips: If you're feeling up to it, it's a good idea to cook and freeze batches of meals for after your baby is born. If not, then this is an excellent favour to ask of family or friends offering to help.

Week 36

Baby is about as long as a stalk of Swiss chard!

48.2cm 2648.9g

What has changed with Baby:

In just a few days Baby's lungs will be fully formed and ready to take their first breath, and her digestive system is now ready to deal with breast milk. Your baby is still putting on weight, and if she hasn't engaged yet will still be shifting her position – although there's not much room to move about!

What has changed with Mummy:

If it hasn't happened already, you'll soon begin to feel your baby start to gradually drop, resulting in increased pressure in your lower belly. The exciting news is that by the end of this week you will be considered full term, and after that your baby could come any day!

How I'm feeling: ....

....

What I've been doing: ....

....

Tips: Relaxing with your hips elevated or using a belly sling could help ease any pelvic pain from the pressure of Baby's head.

Keep Calm and Relax...

Not only is relaxation essential for labour, but being overly worried and stressed can actually delay it from starting. During the birth of your baby your body will cope better if you're calm, and the hormones that help your labour to progress will be released more readily. You could try breathing exercises, gentle stretches or meditation – and creating a calming playlist of music to then listen to during labour can help. Keep a note of the techniques you're planning to try, or those you'd like to research more about.

Signs of Labour

Over these final weeks, you are bound to analyse every ache and twinge wondering if they could be a sign of labour starting. Most aches and pains are due to stretching ligaments and every woman is different, but here are some key early signs of labour:

Higher energy levels:

It's not uncommon for women who have felt worn out or lethargic to experience a sudden burst of energy just before going into labour.

Diarrhoea:

The hormones that cause your uterus to contract can also give you an upset stomach in the hours leading up to your baby's birth. Make sure you drink lots of water if you're affected, and be alert for any further signs of labour.

Contractions:

Labour contractions feel different from Braxton Hicks, which are short and relatively painless tightening sensations. If your contractions build in frequency and intensity, follow the advice from your midwife about when to contact your hospital or birthing centre.

Your waters breaking:

This can happen in a small trickle over a few days as well as one great big gush, and won't necessarily occur for every woman before labour. But if your waters do break this could be a sign that Baby's arrival is imminent, and it's a good idea to call your midwife.

Week 37

Baby is approximately as long as a leek!

49.5cm 2884.8g

What has changed with Baby:

Your baby is full term, and could enter the world any day now. Though some babies are still bald at birth, it's possible that he could be born with hair measuring as much as 3.5 centimetres long! Although he might bide his time for a few weeks yet, he's equipped at last to make his big arrival.

What has changed with Mummy:

Your hospital bag's packed, the nursery is ready and you're all set to finally meet your baby! Call your hospital or midwife at any time if you have any worries about your baby, or about labour and birth, but otherwise sit back and relax as you're about to become a mummy!

How I'm feeling: ....

....

What I've been doing: ....

....

....

Tips: Practise folding up the pram and putting in the car seat a few times before Baby arrives, so that when you're ready to take him home you'll be a dab hand.

38 weeks and beyond

Baby could grow to roughly the size of a pumpkin!

51.2cm   3500g

What has changed with Baby:

Your baby will very soon be in your arms, looking up at you for the first time. Wondering what colour Baby's eyes will be? Most Caucasian babies are born with dark blue eyes, while babies of African or Asian origin will have eyes of dark grey or brown at birth. Their 'true' eye colour may not reveal itself for a few months, so you've got another surprise to come.

What has changed with Mummy:

Most women will go into labour between 37 and 42 weeks of pregnancy, with only around 5% of babies being born on their due date. Unless there are any concerns from your midwife, enjoy the final weeks of being pregnant, safe in the knowledge that your baby is getting stronger by the day.

How I'm feeling: ....

....

What I've been doing: ....

....

....

Tips: Remember to ring your hospital or birthing centre before you leave home if you suspect you're in labour, as this will avoid any unnecessary delays when you arrive.

How to Kick-start Labour

If your due date has come and gone but Baby is showing no signs of exiting, you may want to attempt to speed up the process yourself. Although none are scientifically proven, a lot of mums swear by the following natural remedies, which you might like to try from week 37.

Curry

A lot of women suggest curry as a means to bring on labour, but be wary of eating too much of it if you've been suffering from heartburn. Eating spicy food may stimulate your tummy, and therefore prompt your womb into action.

Pineapple

As well as being both delicious and healthy, pineapple contains the enzyme bromelain - thought to help soften your cervix and bring on labour. Opt for fresh pineapple for maximum effectiveness.

Walking

One theory is that the pressure of your baby's head pressing down on your cervix could stimulate the release of the hormone that causes contractions (oxytocin, otherwise called the love hormone). Don't overexert yourself as you'll need to preserve your energy for labour, but gentle exercise may be beneficial.

Sex

Potentially tricky when you have a big bump, but sex is another thing that could trigger the release of oxytocin. It's best to abstain though if you've been advised to by your doctor or your waters have broken, as it could cause infection.

Use this space to note down your thoughts
and feelings on your third trimester.

....
....
....
....
....
....
....
....
....
....
....
....
....
....
....
....
....
....

Baby Essentials Checklist

When you finally get to bring your baby home, you'll find you need a lot of things to help you feed, bathe, and clothe her – and babies grow really fast! There are many optional extras that can help make your life that bit easier, but here are the basics to act as a starting point.

Clothing:

- Four vests.
- Six one-piece bodysuits for day or night.
- Two cardigans (light wool or cotton are best).
- Six pairs of socks or booties.
- One pair of mittens.
- Hats (broad-brimmed for summer, wool or cotton hat that covers the ears for winter).
- Shawl or blanket.

Bedding:

- Crib, as well as a carry cot or moses basket if you need it.
- Firm, flat mattress which fits well in the crib without leaving space round the edges.
- Four sheets.
- Three light blankets, or a sleeping bag if you prefer.

Changing:

- Changing table or cushioned changing pad.
- Changing bag.
- Nappy cream (for use from two weeks).
- Baby wipes or cotton wool.
- Soft washcloths.
- Newborn-size nappies, reusable or disposable. You'll go through a LOT of these, so stock up!
- Baby soap and powder if you want it.

Feeding:

- If you're planning to breastfeed, nursing bras and maternity pads, as well as a breast pump and milk bags if you'd like to express.
- If bottle-feeding your baby, bottles and teats as well as formula.
- Ten muslin squares.

Bathing:

- Baby bath or bath support.

Other:

- Baby monitor.
- Car seat (you'll need to take this to the hospital ready to bring your baby home!).
- Pram, push chair or buggy suitable from birth.

Welcome to the World!

My baby was born on:

The time was:

....

The place was:

....

Length of labour:

....

Baby is a: ✿ Girl ✿ Boy

Weight:

....

Length:

....

Hair colour:

....

Eye colour:

....

The name I have chosen for my baby:

....

....

Notes

Notes

....

....

....

....

....

....

....

....

....

....

....

....

....

....

....

....

....

....

Notes

Notes

....

....

....

....

....

....

....

....

....

....

....

....

....

....

....

....

....

LTP
1 Coda Studios, 189 Munster Road,
London SW6 6AW
www.littletiger.co.uk

First published in Great Britain 2017

Printed in China • LTP/1800/2082/0917

2 4 6 8 10 9 7 5 3

The information supplied in this journal is not to be used as a substitute
for professional medical care, and does not constitute advice for your
baby or pregnancy. Developmental progress facts detailed within this journal are
general, and are not specific to you or your baby.